Did dinosaurs baby-sit?

Dinosaurs
and Prehistoric Animals

Contents

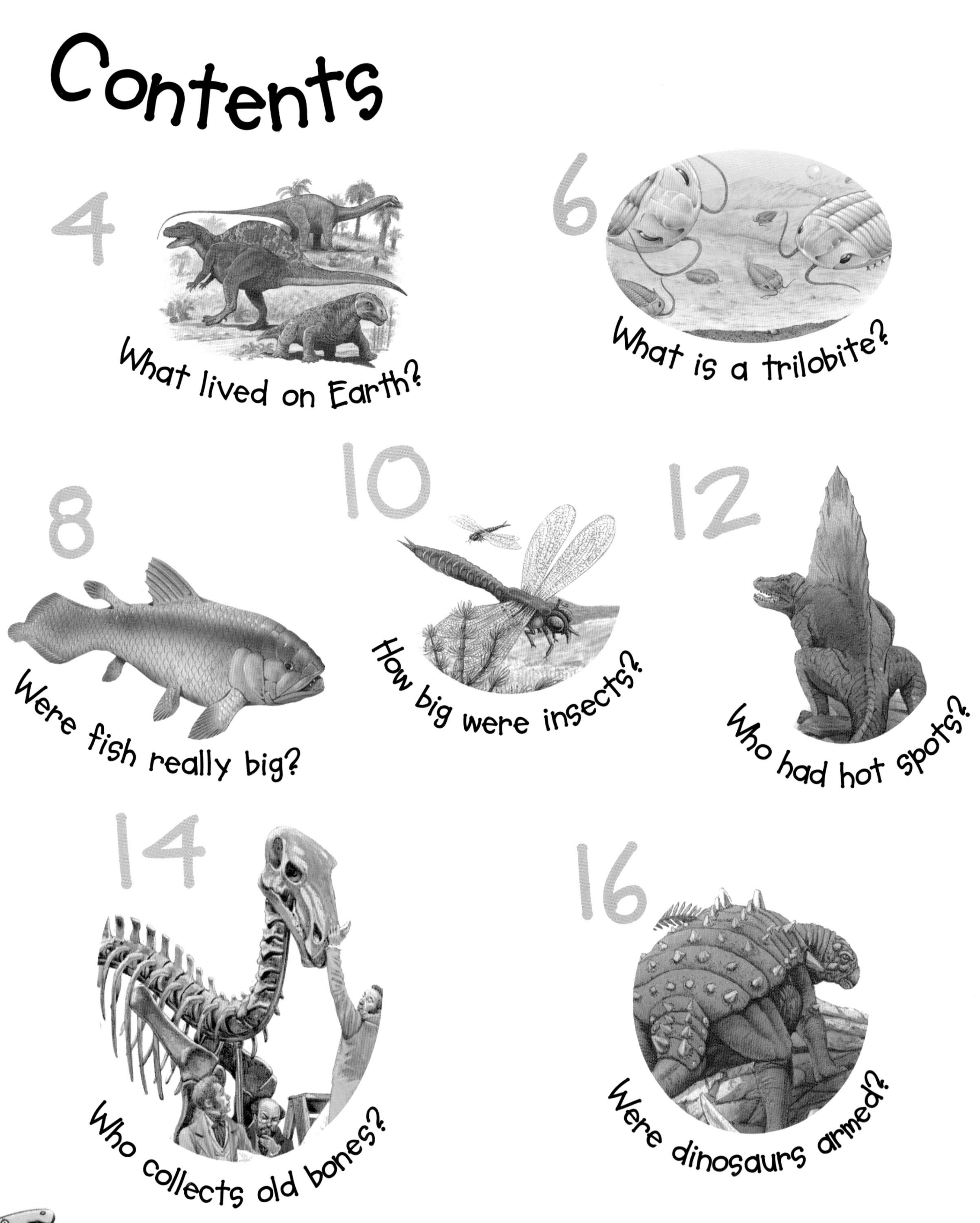

What lived on Earth?

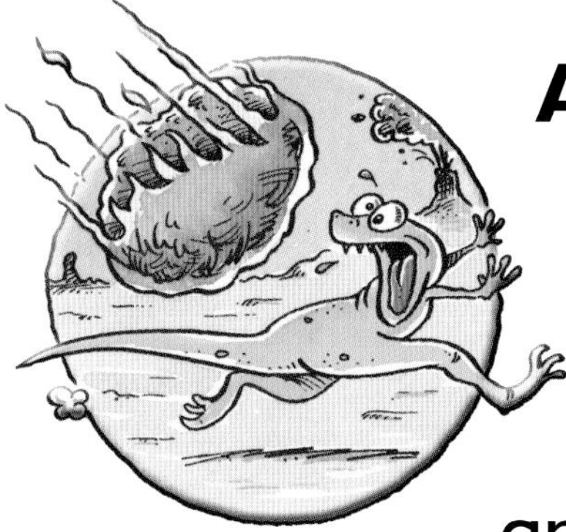

A very long time ago different animals lived on Earth. Then they suddenly vanished. No one is sure why. Perhaps they were hunted by other animals. Maybe the weather became too hot or too cold. Perhaps a meteor hit the Earth or a great flood destroyed them.

In the air

Fierce creatures used to fly in the skies. They were much bigger than birds today.

On land

A group of reptiles called dinosaurs lived on the land. Some were small, the size of chickens; others were huge.

Elasmosaurus

In the ocean

Many animals lived in the oceans. These were early sharks, dolphins, and fish.

Basilosaurus

Plesiosaurus

Did shells zoom?

Yes, and they still do. Small shell-like creatures called *Nautilus* live in the oceans. They move by squirting out jets of water from their shell. This makes them zoom backward.

What can turn animals into stone?

Mud and time. Very long ago, dead animals fell into the sea and were buried under layers of mud. Over time, the mud turned to rock, and the skeleton of the dead animal was trapped in the rock. The animal's remains then also turned to stone. These stones are called fossils.

Do you know?

1. Do we know why some animals disappeared?
2. Can animals be turned to stone?

Answers: 1. No, not for sure. 2. Yes, these are called fossils.

What is a trilobite?

Trilobites looked a bit like wood lice. These little animals swam, crawled, and ran on the seabed a very long time ago. Their bodies had lots of sections and legs. As the trilobite grew, it threw off its old shell for a bigger one. Old shells and dead animals often became fossils, which you can still find today.

Inside out

Trilobites had their skeletons on the outside. This hard covering kept them from being attacked by their enemies.

Stalks and tubes

Sea lilies had a crown of tentacles which they used to trap food. The lilies grew long stalks to attach themselves to the seabed.

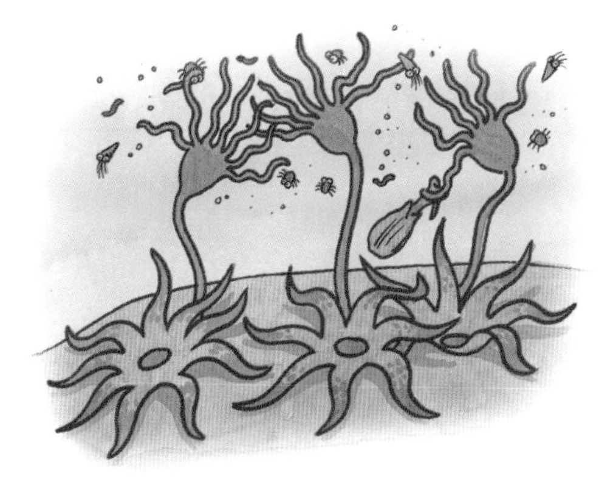

? True or false

Prehistoric sea monsters ate jellyfish.

True. Jellyfish have been around for a very long time. At first they were safe, but later huge fish and sea reptiles would eat the jellyfish.

Can chalk talk?

No, but if it could it would have a lot to tell us! Cliffs made of chalk are very old. They are made of the tiny, crushed-up shells and skeletons of sea animals that lived on Earth long ago.

Is my sponge alive?

It used to be. Sponges come from the ocean. They look like plants, but they're really animals without any heads, arms, or insides. They live on the seabed.

Were fish really big?

Some fish were as big as buses. These early fish had hard, bony, armor-like scales. Some fish even had thick plates like helmets on their heads. Others had fins covered in bone. One giant fish called *Dunkleosteus* had a head the size of a car! Its jaws were lined with bony plates that were like very sharp teeth.

↓ Stinging attack

Jellyfish have been around a long time. They have long, stinging tentacles, which they use to catch food and protect themselves from enemies.

Scary

The huge *Dunkleosteus* roamed the seas. When a fish passed by, it would snap it up in its huge jaws.

Which fish never leave home?

Sea squirts that live in the ocean. Baby sea squirts have fins and swim around like tadpoles. When the young sea squirts lose their tails, they find a home on a rock, crab, or boat, and stick to it for life!

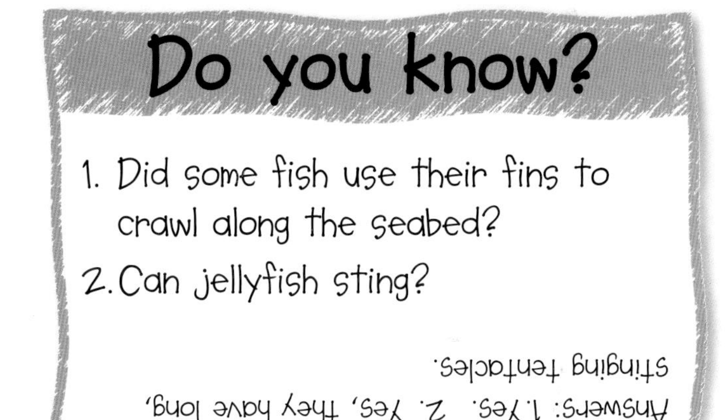

Can fish crawl?

Some scientists believe that long ago fish used their fins to crawl along the bottom of the ocean. These fish were called *Coelacanths*. Scientists thought all these fish had vanished but one was found in 1938.

Coelacanth

How big were insects?

Some insects were the size of birds. Many early insects were much bigger than insects today. We can measure the wings of dragonfly fossils. They had wings as long as those of a seagull. These giant dragonflies zoomed around the swampy forests, eating other insects.

Centipede

Grasshopper

Creepy and crawly

Many insects that you see today also lived on Earth long ago. These include grasshoppers, centipedes, and cockroaches.

Food chain

Plants are eaten by small insects. Insects are eaten by animals such as frogs. Bigger animals eat the frogs. This is called a food chain.

? True or false

Prehistoric trees could catch flies.

True. Prehistoric pine trees oozed a sticky liquid called sap that hardened and became a fossil called amber. Flies and other small insects would land on the trees and get stuck in the sticky sap.

Dragonfly

Cockroach

Giant centipede

Who lays eggs?

Most reptiles lay eggs instead of having babies. Dinosaurs laid their eggs on dry land. Amphibians, like fish, lay their eggs in water.

Who had hot spots?

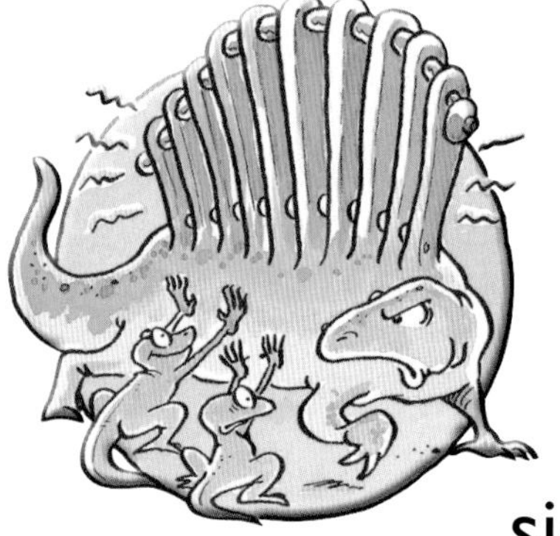

The *Dimetrodon* had a big sail-fin on its back that probably acted like a radiator. If it got cold, the *Dimetrodon* turned sideways to the sun so that the heat warmed up the fin. When *Dimetrodon* was too hot, it turned its back to the sun. It lost heat from the fin and felt cooler.

↑ Fast and slow

Many reptiles, such as crocodiles, move slowly on legs that stick out from their sides. Crocodiles could lift their body off the ground to crawl along. Other reptiles, like dinosaurs, stood up on two back legs.

Did reptiles grow whiskers?

Yes, which made them look more like dogs than lizards. Some reptiles ate plants and dug up roots with their tusk-like teeth. Some were hunters with sharp, biting teeth. They might have looked like this *Thrinaxodon*. These hunters might have used their whiskers like feelers to snuffle their way around.

Thrinaxodon

Can you find fossils?

It's possible to find fossils on the beach, in forests, or in fields. Fossils are found all around the world. A very old fossil was found in Scotland. The fossil was of a little lizard. It was squashed between thin layers of rock like a sandwich filling.

Hot and cold blood

Reptiles are cold-blooded. This means that they need the warmth from the sun to give them energy to move.

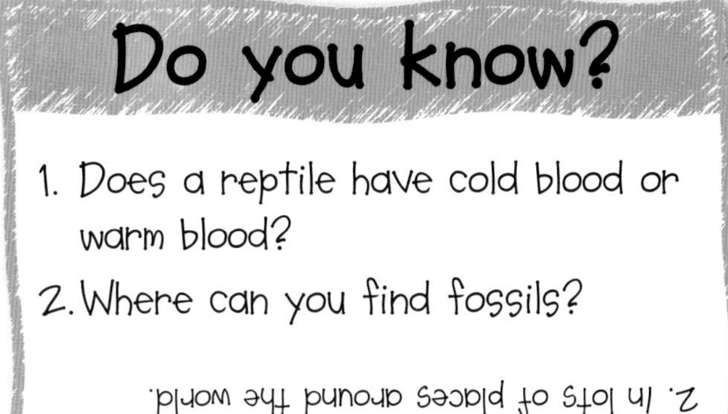

Do you know?

1. Does a reptile have cold blood or warm blood?
2. Where can you find fossils?

Answers: 1. Reptiles have cold blood.
2. In lots of places around the world.

Who collects old bones?

Museums and dinosaur experts!
People are always searching for dinosaur bones. The first dinosaur bones were found many years ago. When the bones of a dinosaur are found, they are put together to make the skeleton of the dinosaur. This shows us what the dinosaur looked like.

Can we make a fossil?

Almost. A copy of a fossil is made by experts when the fossil can't be taken away. Wet plaster is poured over the fossil, like this trilobite below. The shape of the fossil is left in the plaster when it dries.

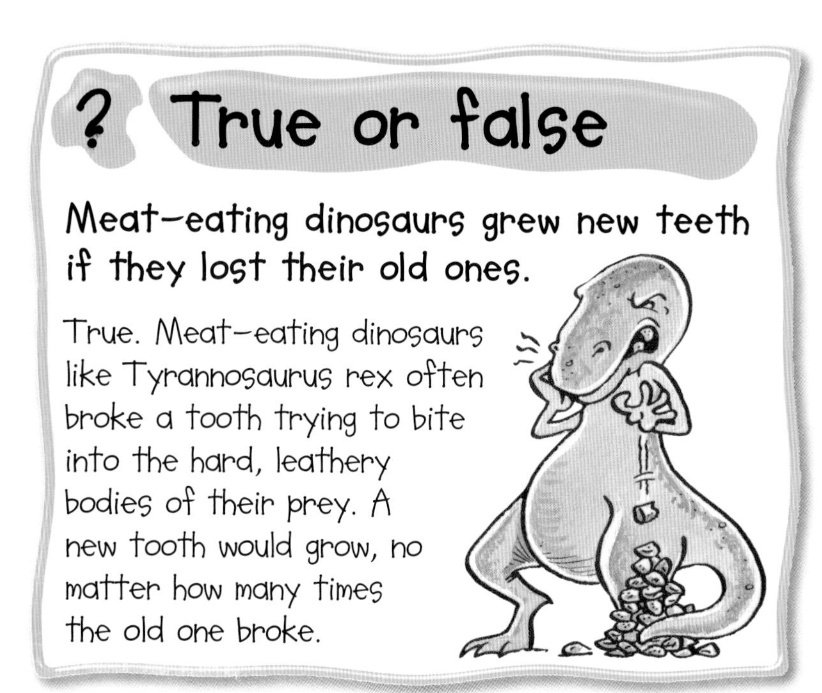

? True or false

Meat-eating dinosaurs grew new teeth if they lost their old ones.

True. Meat-eating dinosaurs like Tyrannosaurus rex often broke a tooth trying to bite into the hard, leathery bodies of their prey. A new tooth would grow, no matter how many times the old one broke.

What were mud swamps?

Mud swamps were like big lakes of thick mud. Fossils are often found near prehistoric mud swamps. Big animals would fall into them and get stuck. If this happened, they would die. Meat-eating dinosaurs would feed on the bodies and then get stuck as well.

Were dinosaurs armed?

Not exactly, but some of them had very dangerous tails! The *Stegosaurus* couldn't run fast to escape its enemies. Instead, it stood still and waved its spiky tail from side to side. The *Diplodocus* lashed its long tail like a whip when attacked. One dinosaur, called *Ankylosaurus,* had a club on the end of its tail.

Diplodocus

Plant-eaters

Some plant-eating dinosaurs swallowed stones with their leaves. The stones helped to mash up the food. *Diplodocus* was a plant-eater.

Stegosaurus

Well-protected

Many dinosaurs had very sharp and dangerous spikes, clubs, and horns for protection.

Which dinosaurs were scary?

Most dinosaurs thought twice before fighting the *Triceratops*. This dinosaur had a horn on its nose and two more horns poking out above its eyes. It also had a row of spikes around its neck collar.

Did dinosaurs baby-sit?

The nest of a *Maiasaura* was 2 meters (7 feet) wide and held up to 30 eggs. The nest was a hole scooped in the ground. The parents watched over the nests to stop other dinosaurs stealing the eggs or trampling on them. The parent dinosaurs would bring their babies food and look after them.

Maiasaura

Which dinosaur had the biggest feet?

Some plant-eating dinosaurs had very big feet. One of the biggest belonged to a duck-billed dinosaur whose footprint was almost three times bigger than an elephant's footprint.

Plant-eating dinosaurs were bigger than meat-eaters.

True. The biggest land animals ever were the plant-eating dinosaurs, such as *Argentinosaurus*. It was ten times heavier than the biggest meat-eating dinosaur, which was the mighty *Tyrannosaurus rex*.

← Dinosaur droppings

Fossilized dinosaur droppings are called coprolites. They look like sausage-shaped pebbles. At one time people thought they were fossilized pine cones!

Which dinosaur laid the biggest egg?

The biggest eggs ever laid belonged to the *Hypselosaurus*. Its eggs were about 30 centimeters (12 inches) long and could hold up to 3 liters (6 pints) of liquid.

What flew in the skies?

Huge flying reptiles soared above prehistoric cliff tops. These flying reptiles called pterosaurs were bigger than any birds. They would swoop down to scoop fish from the waves in their long, pointed jaws. They had enormous wings, and some had long tails that they used to steer themselves as they flew.

Which was the biggest flyer?

A flying reptile that was as big as a small aircraft. It was called *Quetzalcoatlus*. Each wing measured 6 meters (20 feet) across. It was the biggest animal ever to fly in the sky.

→ Flying fish hunters

Fish fossils have been found in some pterosaur stomachs. Pterosaurs could fish as they flew. Their long jaws with saw-like teeth snatched slippery fish out of the water.

Do you know?

1. Were birds the first creatures to fly?
2. Did birds have teeth?

Answers: 1. No, the first creatures to fly were reptiles. 2. Yes.

Did early birds bite?

Some birds may have had teeth. They looked like reptiles with wings. They had scaly legs and a mouth like a dinosaur, with lots of sharp little teeth to catch and eat food.

Gliding

Pterosaurs used rising currents of warm air to help them glide from the top of cliffs into the air. Scientists believe that they would have hunted in groups.

Did sea monsters exist?

Yes, during the age of the dinosaurs. A huge sea reptile called *Tanystropheus* had a neck that was 6 meters (19½-feet) long. It probably used its neck as a kind of fishing rod and dipped its small head into the sea to snatch passing fish in its sharp teeth.

Slow swimmer

The *Tanystropheus* was not a very good swimmer. It would sit in shallow water and grab fish and other sea animals as they passed by. It also hunted on land.

Ichthyosaurus

Tanystropheus

What jumped like a dolphin?

***Ichthyosaurs* jumped and darted through warm ocean waves.** These reptiles were shaped like fish and had big fins, flippers, and flattened tails. They probably swam like dolphins or porpoises and jumped in and out of the sea. They ate fish and smaller reptiles.

? True or false

Plesiosaurs swam like penguins.

True. *Plesiosaurs* had paddle-shaped legs that looked like flippers. *Plesiosaurs* moved their flippers like wings to "fly" through the water. Today, penguins move through the water using their flippers in the same way.

Paddling turtles

Giant turtles sped through the water using their huge front paddles. The *Archelon* grew to 4 meters (13 feet).

Archelon

Who had razor teeth?

***Tyrannosaurus rex,* one of the biggest dinosaurs.** It had powerful jaws and teeth as sharp as razors. It had very big and strong back legs. Its little front arms were small but had sharp pointed claws. The only animal it feared was another *Tyrannosaurus*.

↑ Dead end for dinosaurs

Dinosaurs disappeared a very long time ago. Furry mammals, birds, sea creatures, and a few reptiles lived on. But dinosaurs vanished and have never been seen again. Scientists still don't know why they vanished.

How do we know if dinosaurs ran fast?

Scientists have found out by measuring the distance between the footprints animals left behind. They found that some ran faster than a horse—and some faster than an ostrich!

1. Do some dinosaurs make music?
2. Were all dinosaurs slow?

Answers: 1. Some had head crests that made musical noises. 2. No, some were very fast.

Were dinosaurs musical?

Some dinosaurs may have sounded musical. Duckbills had a huge hollow crest on their head, over 1½ meters (5 feet) long. It looked like a horn sticking out backward. When scientists made a model of the skull and blew through it, it made a noise like a loud trumpet.

After dinosaurs died out, mammals ruled the world. The fiercest hunter was the saber-toothed cat. It looked like a lion without a mane and had two long teeth shaped like daggers as sharp as carving knives. Saber-tooths could open their mouths very wide to hunt and eat larger prey.

Were mammals alone?

No, giant birds stalked the grassy plains and woodlands hunting for food. These big birds could not fly. The *Diatryma* looked like a cross between an eagle and an ostrich and was taller than a human. It would catch animals with its huge claws and hooked beak.

? True or false

Some prehistoric lions had pouches like kangaroos.

True. There were many mammals who were marsupials. This means that they carried their young in pouches. The biggest was the marsupial lion.

New animals

Many animals that came after the dinosaurs looked almost like the animals we see today.

← Mammals

Mammals are warm-blooded and give birth to live young. Many mammals lived with dinosaurs. They looked like rats and ate insects and dinosaur eggs.

Who wore woolly coats?

A very long time ago, elephants had shaggy, woolly coats and were called mammoths. These huge animals lived in snowy forests. They had a layer of fat, a thick yellow undercoat, and a top layer of dark hair to keep them warm. Some had tusks that turned down for digging in the ice.

Tusks for building

Mammoth tusks are long teeth. Prehistoric people used the tusks as tent poles and to make walls for their huts.

Is it a bear or is it a dog?

After the dinosaurs died out, an animal survived that was half bear and half dog. It was as big as a grizzly bear but its head was like a dog's. This animal probably hunted in a pack, like a wolf, and ate plants and meat.

Do you know?

1. Did early elephants have woolly coats?
2. Did some people use mammoth tusks to build tents?

Answers: 1. Yes. 2. Yes, prehistoric people.

Can you eat frozen mammoths?

Deep-frozen mammoths are sometimes dug up. They have been buried in ice for thousands of years. People have even tried eating thawed mammoth steaks!

Who was a heavyweight?

The land mammal that was the biggest of all was a prehistoric rhinoceros called *Baluchitherium*. This heavyweight was bigger than a woolly mammoth and as tall as a giraffe. It lived in Asia and munched leaves from the treetops.

Land bridge

A long time ago, the sea level fell and a land bridge was created between North and South America. Animals crossed from one part to the other.

→ Cave artists

Prehistoric people lived in caves during the Ice Age and drew animal pictures on the cave walls. These pictures show horses, deer, wild cattle, and other animals that the cave people hunted for food.

? True or false

Many mammals were able to fly in prehistoric times.

False. The only flying mammals are bats. They have been on Earth for many years. Bats have lived in the same caves around the world since prehistoric times.

Who was really mixed up?

The *Macrauchenia* had a short trunk like an elephant, the body of a camel without a hump, and the feet and legs of a rhinoceros. It lived in South America, which was then an island. The *Macrauchenia* was tall enough to reach leaves on trees.

Index

This edition published in 2005
Reprinted in 2007, 2008
The Southwestern Company
Nashville, Tennessee

ISBN 978-0-87197-519-5

Produced by Miles Kelly Publishing Ltd
Bardfield Centre, Great Bardfield, Essex CM7 4SL, UK

Publishing Director: Anne Marshall
Designer: Warris Kidwai

Printed in China

Project Director, UK: Fiona Greenland
Editorial Director: Mary Cummings
Managing Editor: Judy Jackson
Copy Editor: Carolyn King
Production Manager: Powell Ropp
Digital Prepress Coordinator: Donna Bailey

The publishers would like to thank the following artists whose work appears in this book: John Butler, Steve Caldwell, Jim Channell, Andrew Clark, Mark Davis, Kuo Kang Chen, Andrew Clark, Peter Dennis, Heather Dickinson, Richard Draper, James Field, Nicholas Forder, Chris Forsey, Mike Foster/Maltings Partnership, Terry Gabbey, Alan Hancocks, Richard Hook, John James, Emma Jones, Tony Kenyon, Aziz Khan, Sue King/SGA, Kevin Maddison, Janos Marffy, Debbie Meekcoms, Helen Parsley, Rachel Philips, Jane Pickering, Neil Reid, Terry Riley, Pete Roberts, Steve Roberts, Peter Sarson, Martin Sanders, Mike Saunders, Sarah Smith, Studio Galante, Rudi Vizi, Mike White, Paul Williams, Peter Wilks.